Night-ti Noises

written by Jay Dale

illustrated by Lesley Danson

"Mum!" said Tessa.
"Why are you here?"

"I came to see if you were cold," said Mum.

"I'm not cold," said Tessa.

"But I can't get to sleep.

There are lots of night-time noises."

A big owl with round eyes went

Toowit! Toowhoo! Toowit! Toowhoo!

"See!" said Tessa.

"I can't sleep with all that noise."

"Come inside," said Mum.
"You can sleep in your bed."

"No!" said Tessa.
"I want to sleep in my new tent."

"Do you want me to sleep
with you?" asked Mum.

"No!" said Tessa.
"I'm a big girl now.
You can go inside."

11

"Oh, no!" said Tessa.

"I can't get to sleep.

There are lots of night-time noises."

"Mum!" shouted Tessa.

"I can't get to sleep!"

CLICK!

The light went on.

Mum came out

to the little tent.

She looked inside.

"Here you are," she smiled.

"I have some ear-muffs for you!"

Tessa gave Mum a big smile.

"Thank you!" she said.

"You are the best mum

in the world!"

15

Then off she went to sleep
in her new tent.

Snore! Snore!